Her heart **pounded** and her hands **trembled** with excitement, though questions filled her head.

KU-042-907

Laura had set herself an incredible **challenge.** She would make the 7000-kilometre journey across the continent from Ecuador to Argentina **alone** and with **no money.**

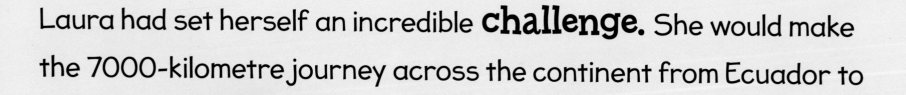

But she was more than a little nervous. With no money, how would she feed herself? Would people be kind? Where would she sleep?

Now that the time was here, Laura really didn't know if she could actually go through with the trip that she had planned so carefully.

ONE GIRL AND HER BICYCLE

ns of Dreams

Written by
Laura Bingham

Illustrated by
Laura Wall

Bradmore Green
Library
020 3700 1003

9/19

26 OCT 2021

18 OCT 2022

2 5 NOV 2022

Please return or renew this book
by the last date printed above.
Renew via phone or online
www.croydon.gov.uk/libraries

CROYDON | Delivering
www.croydon.gov.uk | for Croydon

3 8015 02763 778 8

In **Ecuador,** a country on the west coast of **South America,** a girl stood beside her bike with the vast **Pacific Ocean** behind her.

But deep in her heart, Laura was **determined** to complete her challenge. From her pocket, she pulled a note that her mum had given her.

Laura took a **long, deep breath,** then, with her mum's note safely tucked back into her pocket ...

... she started to **pedal.**

"You **can** do it, Laura!"

she whispered to herself as she started
the **very, very long journey.**

Soon the **Andes** filled the horizon.

As Laura drew closer, her doubts returned. She'd never done anything like this before. Cycling up any one mountain was hard work, never mind the **longest mountain range** in the world!

She stared at the vast peaks ahead, and something caught her eye.

It was an Andean condor.

It **swoop**ed close by.

She was amazed by its **huge** wingspan. The condor soared high above the rocky landscape with such **grace** and **strength.**

"You can do it, Laura!" she told herself again.

"You can **soar** like an Andean condor!"

Laura touched the note nestled in her pocket and, with the **confidence** and **calm** of the condor, she pedalled on ...

... and **on** ...

... and **on.**

Night ...

... after **night.**

Through **storms** ...

... and **sunshine.**

At last!
Laura had **done it!**

She had reached
the **top of the**
mountain and
conquered all her
doubts to get this far!

Laura felt a rush of **happiness** as she flew down the mountain road.

She wished her **family** were with her to share this **wonderful** moment.

Suddenly she realised how much she **missed** them all.

Laura stopped and sat down by the side of the road. She reached into her pocket to comfort herself with the note from her mum.

But her pocket was empty. The note was **gone!**

Laura imagined seeing her family again when she completed her challenge.

The thought filled her with a warm glow of **love** and **happiness.**

She realised that she didn't need the note after all.

The **love** and **support** of her family were **always** with her!

With the **enthusiasm** and **determination** to complete her goal restored, Laura continued her journey.

After so many days of cycling, Laura was **exhausted** and she began to **wobble** right and then left.

A car sped past, almost knocking her off her bicycle as she weaved in the road.

Laura knew that if she were to stay safe, she would need to **eat** and **rest** again soon.

WHOOSH!

But where?

It was too **dangerous** to cycle here when she was so tired and it was certainly not a safe place to rest!

So she pushed her bike up the mountain, hoping that she would soon find somewhere to stop.

At the top, Laura found a safe place to rest. She sat down wearily and slowly ate a bread roll. It wasn't much, but she savoured every crumb.

This was the last of her food.

Drawing on the little energy she had left, she cycled on. Laura was worried about finding a place to sleep. She was a **stranger** to the people of Ecuador ...

... and she hoped they would be friendly.

Just as the sun was setting, Laura saw a small group of houses ahead. She had a **nervous,** tingly feeling in her stomach. But she chose a house, took a deep breath and **tried to smile** as she knocked on the door. Tears rolled down Laura's face as she was **turned away.**

It had taken lots of courage to knock on that door, but she would have to be **brave** and try again ...

... and again.

Tired and hungry, Laura was about to give up, when a kind-looking woman opened the door of the last house.

Laura wiped away her tears and did her best to smile a friendly greeting. The woman **smiled** back! Laura beamed, feeling her own **inner sunshine** glow brightly once again.

The woman invited Laura into her home, where a **delicious-smelling** meal was being cooked.

Though she was a stranger and they had little to share, the woman's family greeted Laura warmly. She was so **grateful** for their **kindness.**

The family let Laura pitch her tent in the **safety** of their garden.

With a full tummy, she stretched out to **rest** and thought of the condor and of her mum's note, and how they'd helped her on her way.

The next morning, Laura was **full of energy.**
She thanked the kind family and set off once more. Laura had
come such a long way already, but she knew her journey had only
really just begun – the **jungles of Peru** awaited her!

Ecuador "I can and I will!"

So that was the start of my adventure!

At the age of 22, I set off to cycle through South America with no money, relying on my own survival skills and the help of strangers. It was a big dream, but I love a challenge!

My main aim was to raise money and awareness for the charity Operation South America, who look after vulnerable young girls in Paraguay. Life can be incredibly tough for the children of South America, but by buying this book, you've helped them too, as a donation will be made to Operation South America for every book sold.

It took me 26 days to cycle across Ecuador, travelling a total of 783 km! Some days I stopped and rested, and other days I spent time helping the people who had been so kind to me.

Do you recognise this scene from the story?

I hope you'll join me on my next adventure as I cycle across Peru, where I share my journey with a very exciting travelling companion!

Plan your own adventure!

Your adventure can be as big or as small as you like –
a camping trip in the wild or closer to home, or just a
day out. You can plan your adventure in as much detail
as you like, but here are some important questions you
might want to think about to get you started.

What will your adventure be?

Why do you want to do it?

What problems might you face?

How will you get there?

What will you need?

Who will go with you?

"*Perseverance* is the difference between
those who make it and those who don't."
Laura Bingham

Did you spot these animals in the story?

Andean condor

The Andean condor is one of the largest flying birds in the world. With a wingspan of over 3 metres, it's as wide as two 10-year-olds standing with their arms outstretched!

Llama

Llamas are shy, gentle animals that can be very curious. They live in mountainous places and are very intelligent, and can be trained to pull a cart and carry packs.

Northern pudú

Pudú are the smallest deer in the world. When fully grown they are only a little taller than the length of your school ruler! They are excellent climbers, strong jumpers and very fast.

ISBN 978-1-78270-343-3

Text and expedition photographs copyright © Laura Bingham
Illustrations copyright © Laura Wall
Photograph of Laura Bingham (p30 tl) by Brandon Giesbrecht

Animal photographs (l–r): TravelStrategy/Shutterstock.com, Mark Pitt Images/Shutterstock.com, Patricio Pillajo

Every effort has been made to trace the copyright holders and obtain permission to reproduce the photographs used in this book. Please do contact the publisher with any enquiries or information relating to the images or the rights holders.

All rights reserved. No part of this publication may be reproduced or utilised in any form or by any means electronic or mechanical, including photocopying, recording, or by any information storage and retrieval system now known or hereafter invented, without the prior written permission of the publisher and copyright holder.

First published 2019

Published by Award Publications Limited, The Old Riding School, Welbeck, Worksop, S80 3LR

191

Printed in Turkey